6
six

7
seven

8
eight

9
nine

10
ten

DAINGEA
9 NOV 2021
WITHDRAW
D0590755

Can you count?

2 ducks

5 apples

3 cars

8 butterflies

1 2 3 4 5

How many strawberries are there?

How many cupcakes can you see?

How many teddy bears are there?

6 7 8 9 10

Big and small

big

Small

Which animal is the biggest?

Which animal is the smallest?

A lot, a little, none

A lot   **A little**   **None**

More or less?

Are there more socks or more gloves?

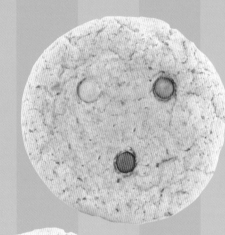
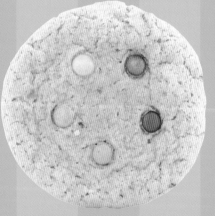

Which biscuit has the most sweets?

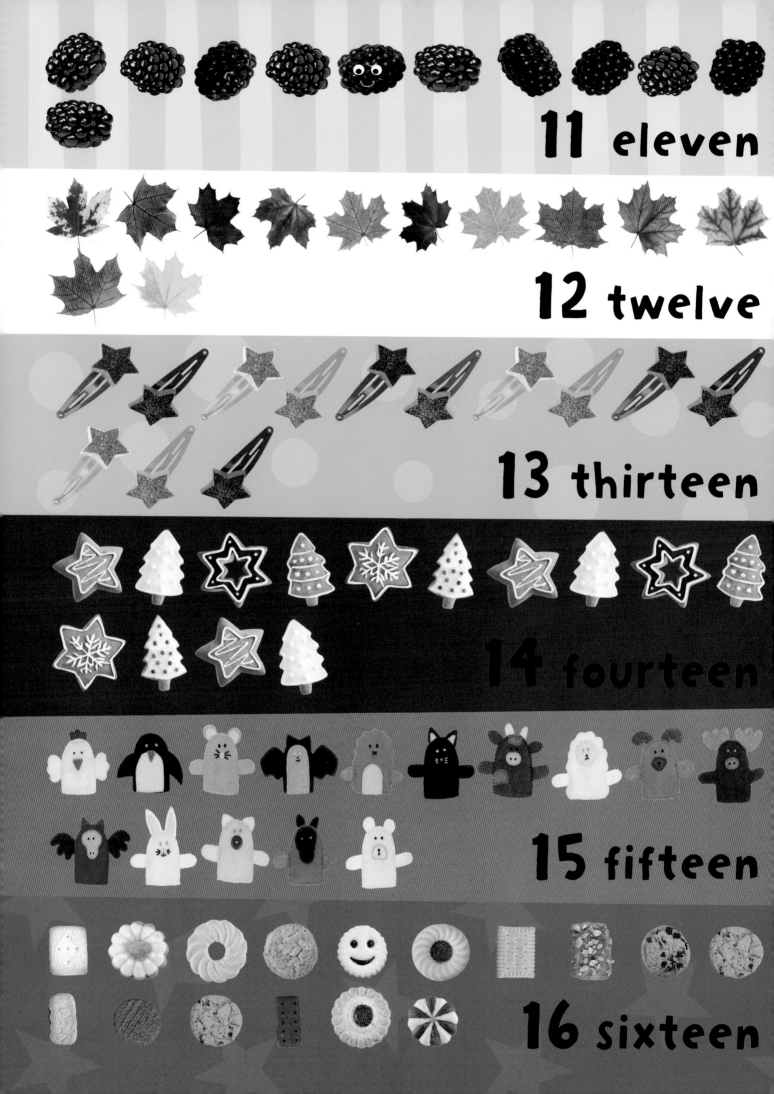

11 eleven

12 twelve

13 thirteen

14 fourteen

15 fifteen

16 sixteen

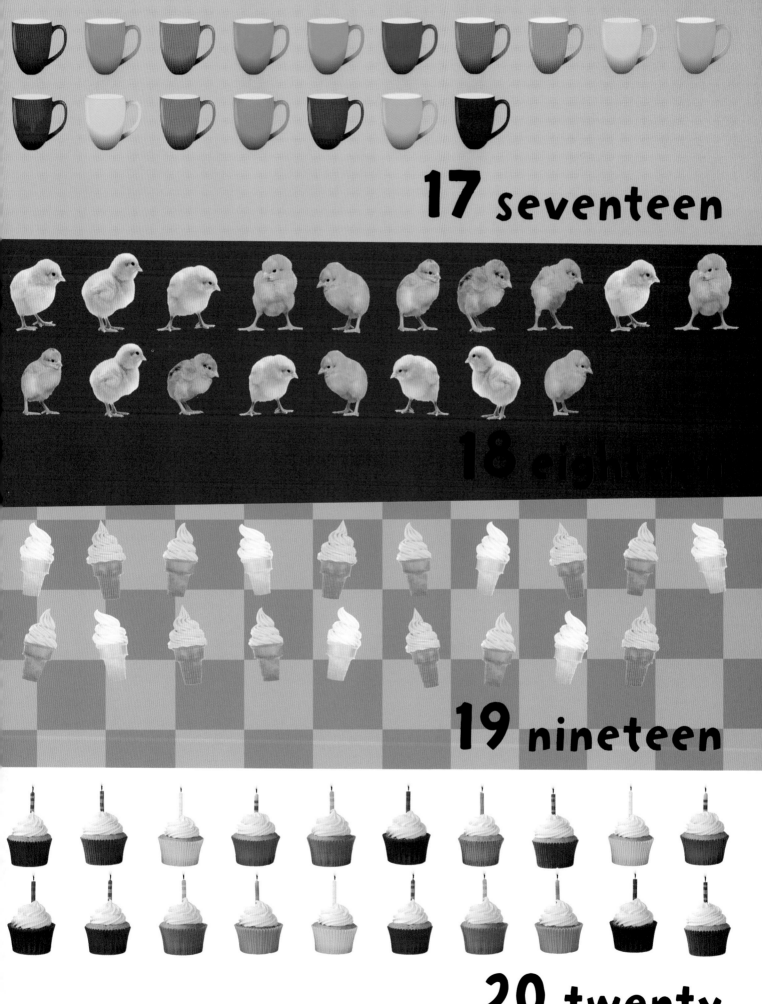

17 seventeen

18 eighteen

19 nineteen

20 twenty

Can you add?

How many ladybirds
are on the leaf?

How many
ladybirds are
not on the leaf?

How many ladybirds
are there all together?

How many red
peppers are there?

How many green
peppers are there?

How many peppers are there all together?

30 thirty

40 forty

50 fifty

60 sixty

70 seventy

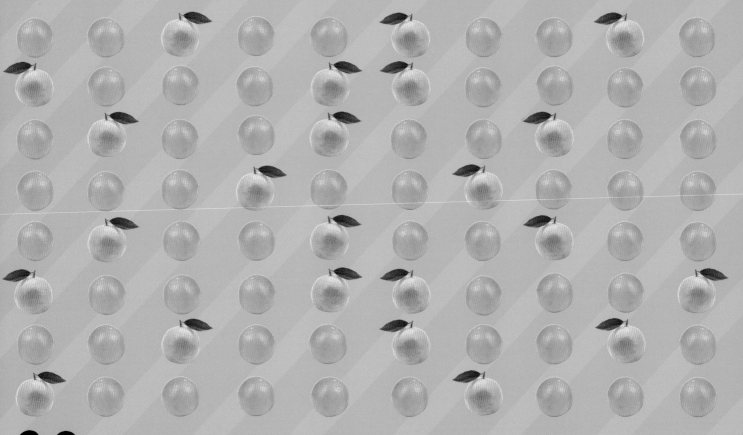

80 eighty

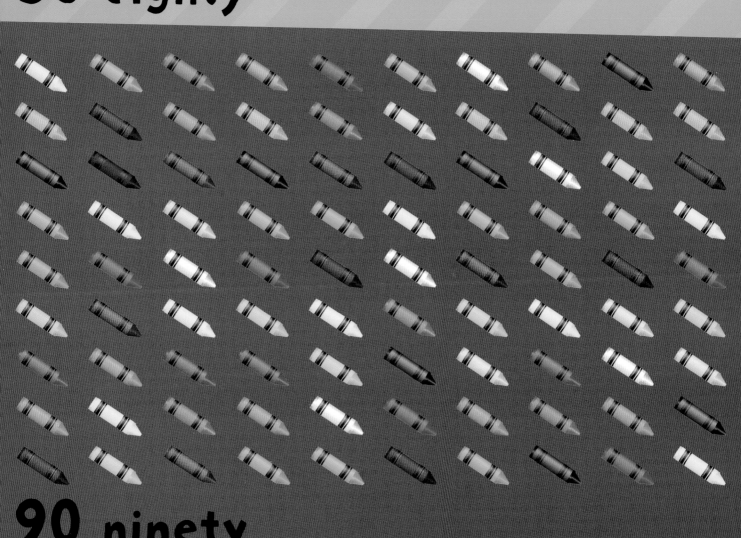

90 ninety

100 one hundred

How many pink sweets can you see?

How many sweets are round?